Sam & The Global Goals

Adventures in a Better World

Daniel Thomas

ISBN: 9798346245889

Dedication

This book is dedicated to my parents, grandparents, aunts, uncles, teachers, Troop 1905, Longhorn Council, and Scouting America.

Table of Contents

Acknowledgements

I'm grateful to have learned about the UN's Sustainable Development Goals and our collective efforts to improve the lives of people everywhere and protect the environment.

The UN Sustainable Development Goals (SDGs) are a set of 17 goals designed to make the world a better place by 2030. They aim to end poverty, protect the planet, and ensure everyone enjoys peace and prosperity. Each goal focuses on different areas like clean water, quality education, and good health. Think of them as a big to-do list for the world to help people live better lives and take care of our Earth. The goals encourage countries to work together to achieve these important changes.

I am deeply grateful to Mrs. Avalyn Pace, and Mrs. Linda Abramson Evans of UNA Dallas Board, who are industry leaders and educators who have devoted their time and passion to implement the SDGs in Dallas focusing on human rights, refugee crises, climate change, and gender equality. They have worked tirelessly to bring together youth, non-profits, clubs, universities, and businesses to create an environment of hope.

I'm also fortunate to have met and interacted with Maria Amalla the Manager of Grassroots Advocacy at UNA. Her dedication to mobilizing members, and her strong commitment to the principles of the UN, even through national budget cuts and challenging times, have shown me what it means to lead with purpose despite setbacks.

Mrs. Pace, Mrs. Evans, and Mrs. Amalla are committed in giving their time to others. Their passion and leadership have greatly shaped my understanding and strengthened my determination to make a positive impact.

Prologue

Sam Discovers the Goals

Prologue: Sam Discovers the Goals

It was beautiful, sunny afternoon when Sam decided to climb to the attic of his grandmother's house. He stumbled upon a thick dusty book amongst boxes of old clothes and forgotten treasures.

Sam's curiosity grew as dust flew through the air when he opened the enormous cover of the book. Suddenly, as if a switch had been flipped, a swirl of bright blue light emerged from the book and encompassed Sam in a sparkling embrace. In an instant, he was gone; the attic dissolved before his eyes. Before him stood a vibrant village filled with people, laughter, and color.

"Welcome to the World of the Global Goals!" A jovial man, spreading warmth with his smile said. "I am Mr. Hope. Come, let me show you how we are working together to make the world a better place."

Sam's mouth fell open in astonishment. "Wow! This is amazing! Where do we get started?"

"Every amazing adventure starts with a first step," Mr. Hope said.

"Let me take you to the first Goal: No Poverty."

Sam's heart raced. He turned to the reader, and with an expressive face, said, "Come on, let's go see what the Global Goals hold together!"

Chapter 1

No Poverty

Chapter 1: No Poverty

Food for Everyone: At a community center, Sam watched volunteers give food to people who were from the same area. "C'mon," Mr. Hope said. "Every family who lives here gets food. Do you want to help?"

"Yes!" said Sam, and they started to serve food. Sam was serving soup to children who had smiles that lit up their whole face. The kids' parents watched Sam serve with grateful looks filled with warmth and appreciation.

"Wow! This food is delicious," Sam said as they tasted it a little for themselves. "People seem really happy."

"Good food can bring us all together," Mr. Hope said, nodding.

Jobs for Parents: Mr. Hope took Sam to the workshop room to see parents learning skills. "These parents are learning skills to get training for good jobs," Mr. Hope explained.

There were people in the workshop making beautiful things, and some parents were practicing making bracelets right in front of Sam's eyes. "Not only is it fun to make things, they can sell them and make money too," Sam said.

Safe Homes: Later they traveled a little further to see a neighborhood of new homes. "Come see the new homes that are being built!" Mr. Hope exclaimed. Sam saw families moving into strong homes, lots of families had cheerful gardens!

Sam watched some of the kids playing in their new yards and said, "Everyone should have a right to live in a safe place." "That's true," Mr. Hope said. "And, a safe home is where it starts to better lives."

Free School Supplies: They went to a school not too far away, and Sam helped give away huge bright backpacks that were filled with school supplies! "Now, all the kids will be able to start school feeling prepared," Sam said as they gave the backpack to a little girl who hugged the backpack in delight.

The girl turned to tell her group of friends, "I love my new bag!"

Community Gardens: "Let's plant some vegetables!" Mr. Hope exclaimed. Sam dug into the ground while putting in seeds for food that would grow that was fresh and good for the community.

"This will be an amazing garden," said Sam as they wiped off their sweat from their forehead. "I'm looking forward to it growing."

Chapter 2

Zero Hunger

Chapter 2: Zero Hunger

Next, Sam met Chef Nourish in an idyllic field of golden wheat.

School Meals: "We at school make sure that all the children will be looked after," said the chef. The students enjoyed the meals Sam provided them which were all well balanced.

"These lunches are really nourishing and delicious!" said Sam, seeing the expression of joy on kids' faces.

Farm Aid: "We provide our farmers with better seeds and better tools!", Chef Nourish explained. The crops grew well with the hands of farmers, as Sam watched.

"This will feed a lot of people!" shouted Sam, admiring the tall green stalks of corn.

Food Banks: Sam helped organize the shelves of a food bank. "This is the place where families who don't have enough to eat come to," said Chef Nourish.

Feeling proud about stocking shelves with donated goods, Sam said, "It feels really good to help other people get food."

Healthy Breakfasts: “Breakfast is a vital meal!” Chef Nourish said as Sam helped make the healthy breakfasts in the morning.

"This oatmeal is delicious and packed with energy!" Sam said while serving bowls to hungry kids.

Local Markets: Sam had visited a busy farmer's market. "When you sell fresh produce, it makes your community a healthier, happier place," said chef nourish.

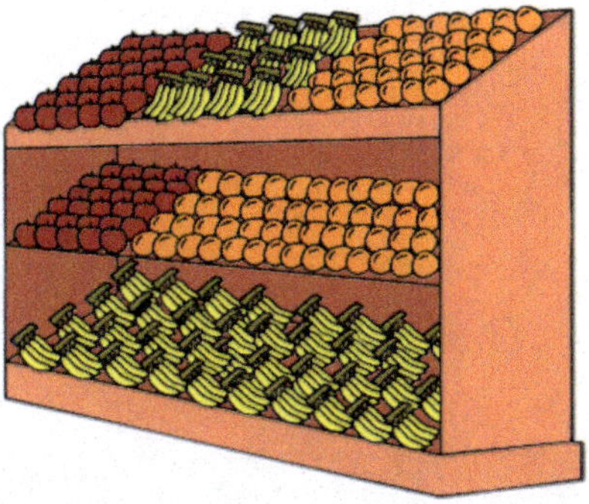

Sam enjoyed picking out ripe fruits and veggies at the farmers market. "These markets are so vibrant and enjoyable," said Sam.

Chapter 3

Good Health & Well-Being

Chapter 3: Good Health & Well-being

Dr. Care welcomed Sam to a bright, busy hospital.

Vaccines for Everyone: "Vaccines protect everyone from illnesses," Dr. Care explained. Sam watched as children bravely got their shots.

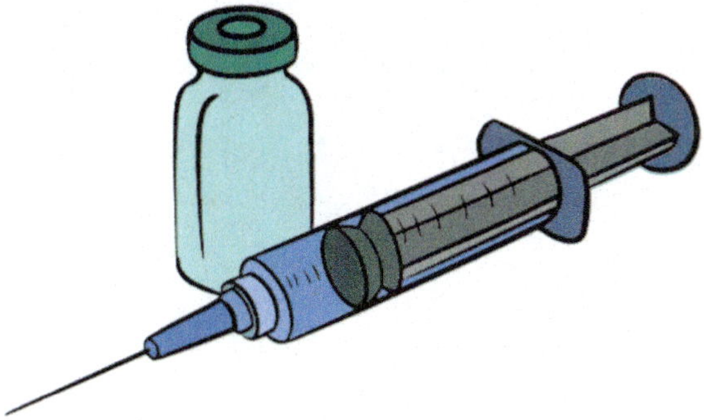

"You are very brave," Sam held the hand of a frightened little boy who got his shot.

"Thank you Sam, but it didn't hurt at all though!" the little boy gently smiled.

Clean Water: “Clean water is important to good health,” Dr. Care explained. With his assistance, Sam helped to install new water filters in the village.

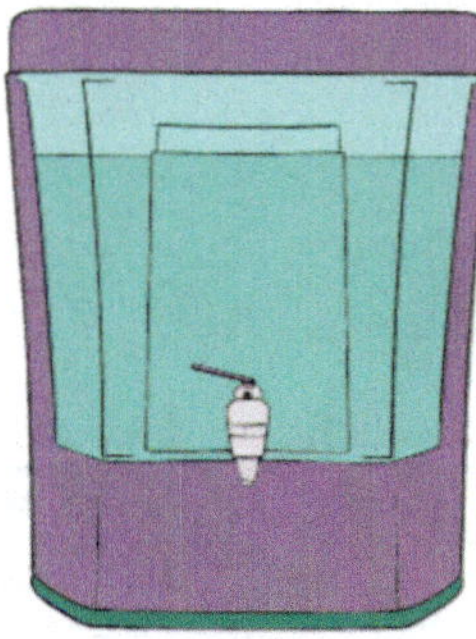

“Now everybody can drink safely,” Sam proudly said after helping them.

Exercise Fun: "Exercise is important", said Dr. Care as he began the dance-a-thon with the kids.

Sam joined in with the kids and laughed and danced. "This is so fun and REALLY great for us", said Sam.

Mental Health Support: "Talking about how you feel is okay" said Dr. Care. When he looked into the office he saw the mental health counselors assisting children to talk about their feelings.

"Talking helps me a lot" Sam said. He was very thankful for the mental health counseling to talk about his feelings.

Doctor Visits: "Regular check-ups help keep

us healthy" said Dr. Care. Sam had helped coordinate a health fair where families had access to doctors and the billing was done so no one ended up paying anything that day.

"I want everyone to be healthy", Sam said while handing out fliers for the health fair.

Chapter 4

Quality Education

Chapter 4: Quality Education

Ms. Bright ushered Sam into a new and lively classroom with kids eagerly waiting.

New Schools: "We are building schools everywhere," Ms. Bright shared. Sam mingled with the children while painting walls and arranging classrooms in a new school.

"These kids are going to love their new school," Sam thought to himself, taking in the bright, colorful rooms.

Books *for* Everyone: "Books will give you new worlds," Ms. Bright told Sam as he was handing out colorful storybooks to enthused, excited children.

"I can't wait to read this!" one child said, hugging the book to their chest.

Training Teachers: "Good teachers make all the difference," Ms. Bright said as Sam observed teachers learning how to make lessons more fun and engaging.

"I love how much teachers can do when provided with the support they need," said Sam.

School Supplies: "Each student needs the right tools," Ms. Bright said as Sam handed out notebooks, pencils, and crayons.

"It looks like we're all ready to learn now," said Sam, noticing the kids' eyes light up.

Learning for Everyone: "Everyone deserves the right to learn," Ms. Bright explained. Sam organized a separate classroom with desks, typewriters, computers and supplies for children with disabilities.

"Now everyone belongs," Sam said, smiling as they watched children engage in thoughtful learning together.

Chapter 5

Gender Equality

Chapter 5: Gender Equality

Ms. Equal exposed Sam to a circle of passionate and focused girls and boys.

Girls in School: "Girls deserve education too, just like boys," said Ms. Equal. Sam watched as the girls laughed and danced towards the school.

"Learning is for everyone!" Sam shouted, giving high-five's to girl students.

Ending Child Marriage: "We are trying to end child marriage, " Ms. Equal shared. Sam joined a community meeting where everyone was talking about why girls should be in school instead of getting married.

"Everyone deserves to grow up and make their own choices," Sam said.

Equal Pay: "Women and men should have equal pay for equal work," said Ms. Equal. Sam was able to meet women who happily shared stories about getting equal pay.

"That's fair!" he exclaimed, "It's nice to see equality at work."

Women Leaders: "Women can also be leaders!" said Ms. Equal. Sam had the chance to talk with women leaders of businesses and communities.

"You inspire me!" he said to them, “I hope to be a leader like you one day.”

Sharing Chores: "Everyone should help each other at home!" said Ms. Equal. Sam helped families to create chore charts that shared the work evenly.

"Teamwork makes the dream work!" Sam said when he saw families sharing work together on the same chores.

Chapter 6

Clean Water & Sanitation

Chapter 6: Clean Water and Sanitation

Mr. Pure took Sam to the shining stream and busy settlement.

Clean Water Access: Mr. Pure spoke of access to clean water: "we make sure everyone has clean water;" while Sam helped in laying pipes to allow fresh water into people's homes.

Sam felt he was contributing to everyone being able to drink safely, thereby preserving their health.

Building Toilets: "Our village remains clean because we have toilets," Mr. Pure explained. Sam was building sturdy toilets for their village.

"This will keep everyone in the community healthy," Sam proclaimed, as he fully understood the need for sanitation.

Water Filters: "The filters purify the water and make the water safe to drink," said Mr. Pure. However, Sam was physically demonstrating to families on how to operate the new water filters.

"These water filters are lifesavers," Sam declared. He was excited to see clean water flowing from the filters.

Handwashing Stations: "Washing hands prevents illness," said Mr. Pure. Sam helped set up handwashing stations at schools.

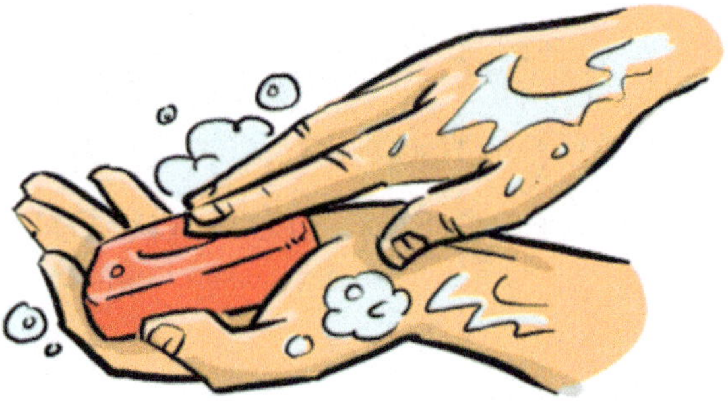

"Now everyone can keep the illness away-," said Sam, as he was showing others how to operate the stations.

Protection of Water Sources: "We should keep the rivers clean," said Mr. Pure. Sam participated in a team that was cleaning up litter in a nearby river.

"Clean water is vital!" Sam declared. He picked up litter with the clean-up team.

Chapter 7

Affordable & Clean Energy

Chapter 7: Affordable & Clean Energy

Mr. Bright showed Sam a field of brilliant solar panels.

Solar energy: "The solar panels use the suns energy to give us a clean energy," Mr. Bright explained. Sam assisted to install solar panels on rooftops.

"This sun energy's incredible!" said Sam, amazed at how the solar panels made millions of particles of electricity.

Wind Turbines: "The wind turbines produce wind energy," Mr. Bright explained to Sam, who was visiting a wind energy farm. Sam could feel the wind blowing around him.

"How amazing that the wind energy is powering the TVs and all the other homes?" Sam wondered.

Energy for All: "Electricity is not a luxury, but a need for all people," Mr. Bright said passionately. Sam was part of a team who brought solar lanterns to poor people in remote villages and was overjoyed at the differences these would make.

"These lamps will light up the darkness,", he said as he watched the villagers' faces light up with joy.

Energy Efficient Homes: "Conserving energy is always smart," Mr. Bright said. Sam helped to insulate people's homes and observed first hand that they were warmer in the winter and cooler in the summer.

"These homes feel so cozy now," Sam noted as he felt the difference.

Clean Cooking Stoves: "Clean cooking stoves are healthier," Mr. Bright said based on his experience. Sam helped several families switch from their dirty cooking stoves to clean cooking stoves because they are healthier.

"I think I can cook with this stove now. It's so much safer and easier," said Sam as he tasted a fantastic meal cooked on the new stove.

Chapter 8

Decent Work & Economic Growth

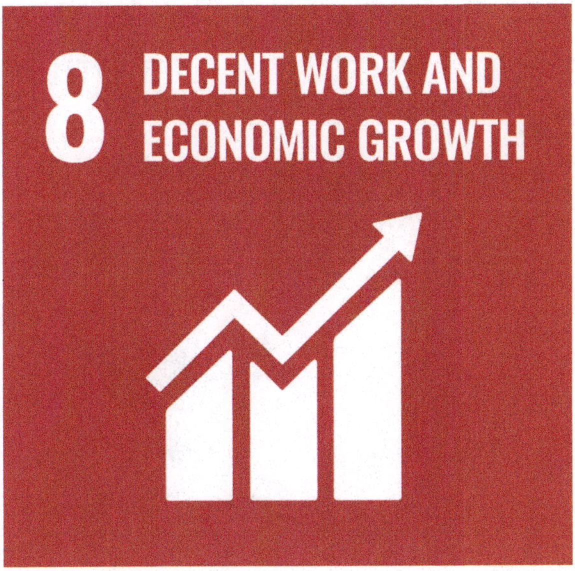

Chapter 8: Decent Work & Economic Growth

Madam Progress assisted Sam on a bright and bustling market day.

Good Jobs: "Everyone deserves a good job," Ms. Progress said. Sam saw a variety of people working in stores and offices, and getting paid for it.

"These jobs support families," he said, appreciating the thriving market.

Small Business: "Small businesses support families grow," Madame Progress said. Sam assisted in opening a small family run bakery.

"This smell of the bakery is so good!" Sam said, enjoying the fresh bread of the bakery.

Youth Training: "We need to teach youth skills for tomorrow," Madam Progress said. Sam signed up for a youth workshop to teach skills to teens.

"Learning new things is exciting," Sam said, working with carpentry tools.

Safe Workplaces: "Workplaces should be safe," Madame Progress said. Sam took part as a safety inspector to see if factories were following safety regulations and laws.

"All workplaces should be safe," Sam reminded himself, checking to be sure everything was correct.

Fair trade: "Farmers make money from fair trade," Madame Progress said. Sam visited at a fair trade coffee farm where he saw farmers paid good prices for their goods.

"Fair trade helps everyone," said Sam sipping his fair trade coffee.

Chapter 9

Industry, Innovation, & Infrastructure

Chapter 9: Industry, Innovation, and Infrastructure

Sam was welcomed by Engineer Innovate at a busy construction area.

Bridges and Roads: Engineer Innovate said, "Good infrastructure connects us." Sam took part in designing a new bridge.

"I'm excited about my contribution because it allows countless other people to get to work and school," said Sam with pride.

Internet for All: "The internet opens the door to the world," Engineer Innovate explained. Sam helped develop plans to provide broadband in remote areas, when internet access is scarce.

"Now everyone can connect and learn," Sam said on a video call with new friends.

Public Transport: "Public transport helps to reduce traffic congestion," Engineer Innovate said. Sam rode some new buses that made it easier and cleaner for people to travel.

"This is fantastic," exclaimed Sam while enjoying the pleasant experience.

Green Buildings: "Sustainable buildings are energy-efficient," Engineer Innovate explained. The green buildings that Sam visited used less energy and less materials.

"These buildings are architectural possibilities of what's to come!" said Sam while admiring the design.

Recycling Center: "Recycling saves waste," Engineer Innovate said, while Sam created collection points with support from the community, where objects could be recycled.

"This is helping save our planet," Sam said, while sorting recyclables with the community.

Chapter 10

Reduced Inequalities

Chapter 10: Reduced Inequalities

Ms. Fair showed Sam a vibrant community and other people, giving everyone an opportunity to belong.

Equitable Opportunity: "Everyone has equitable opportunity," said Ms. Fair, Sam saw existing schools and workplaces with equitable opportunity for everyone.

"This is great," said Sam, feeling excitement seeing everyone learning and working together.

Anti-discrimination Laws: “Laws assist in protecting all of us,” explained Ms. Fair, Sam learned about laws that provide protection to people by ensuring fairness.

“Those laws are a good thing!, exclaimed Sam reflecting back on the a laws that influence, support and assist people.

Accessible Public Space: “Spaces should be accessible to all people in the public space”, said Ms. Fair. Sam helped create ramps and accessibility related to public spaces.

"Now people can access these places," said Sam when he was testing the ramps that that he helped build.

Support For Refugees: "Refugees need support", said Ms. Fair. Sam supported refugees and welcomed them as they search for homes and jobs.

"Everyone deserves a second chance especially with the stories we have heard," empathized Sam in light of what they had shared.

Community Centers: "Community centers provide belonging", said Ms. Fair. Sam organized events, like arts and crafts at the local community center, so that everyone could attend.

"This is a great place of belonging for every-one," exclaimed Sam, as he looked around at all the people at the community center.

Chapter 11

Sustainable Cities & Communities

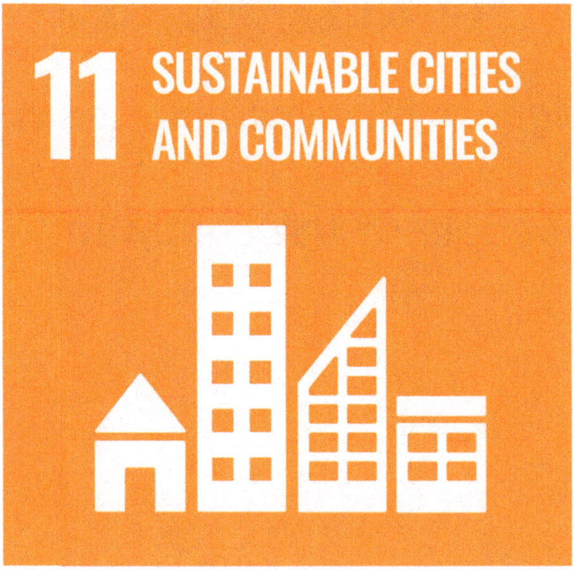

Chapter 11: Sustainable Cities & Communities

Planner Green provided Sam with examples of green cities and new ideas.

Public Parks: "Parks are the lungs of cities," Planner Green said. Sam worked with others to plant small trees and beautiful flowers in a new public park.

"This is going to be a beautiful place for everybody," Sam said, taking in a deep breath of fresh air.

Affordable Housing: "Everybody needs a place to live," Planner Green said. Sam helped in building low income homes for families.

"Now more people can have a place to live safely," said Sam with pride in the work they had done.

Bike Lanes: "Bike lanes make cities safer and cuts down on traffic," Planner Green said. Sam was riding bikes in the new bike lanes, which helped people ride bikes with safety.

" I love riding bikes! It is also eco friendly," Sam shouted out during the ride.

Waste Management: "Waste management is very important" Planner Green said. Sam got the community started with recycling programs, and developed composting programs.

"This helps lessen our footprint on the environment," Sam said while putting waste aside with neighbors.

Clean Air Initiatives: "Clean air is very important", Planner Green stated. Sam worked with others to plant trees to increase awareness for clean energy, and worked to lower air pollution.

"It feels awesome breathing fresh air", concluded Sam, enjoying the breeze.

Chapter 12

Responsible Consumption & Production

Chapter 12: Responsible Consumption & Production

Ms. Sustain instructed Sam about how to reduce waste and smartly use resources.

Recycling Programs: Ms. Sustain stated, "This recycling is for the good of our planet." Sam set up recycling points in schools with the hope that the schools will incentivize and encourage everyone to recycle items where and when they can.

Sam was happy to see, "these bins are filling up quickly." This could never had happened without the engagement of the students.

Reusable Bags: Ms. Sustain instructed Sam to “Say no to single-use plastics.” Sam was handing out reusable bags at a market, reducing the amount of plastics used as single-use bags.

Sam commented, “these ones are really strong and they will hold a lot,” while using the reusable bag to collect groceries at the market.

Composting: Ms. Sustain explained, “Waste becomes resources when we compost.” Sam was composting kitchen waste to help families produce nice soil to grow plants and vegetables.

Sam was very excited to see, "This is how nature does it!" as the green plants started to grow from composted soil.

Eco-Friendly Products: Ms. Sustain asked Sam if he would, "make sure that if they buy things, that they are kind to the Earth, and having products help save the Earth." Sam was educating shoppers to use eco-friendly supplies in shops.

Sam noticed a store with, “These things will save our planet” when seeing all of the eco-friendly products on display.

Reducing Food Waste: Ms. Sustain stated, “When we throw food away, we are actually throwing Earth’s resources away.” Sam offered some suggestions on how they could reduce food waste in their homes and schools.

When helping many families, Sam said, “We all can make a difference,” when helping families make smarter choices to take action using food waste.

Chapter 13

Climate Action

Chapter 13: Climate Action

Captain Planet called on Sam to help him on a mission to save the Earth from climate change.

Tree Planting: “Trees absorb carbon dioxide,” said Captain Planet. Sam planted trees in areas where they were cut down, providing carbon reduction to the environment.

"These trees can help the planet breathe," said Sam, *feeling* the soil in their hand.

Energy Conservation: “Every little bit helps,” said Captain Planet. Sam turned off lights and unplugged electronics when they were not using them. "Saving energy was pretty easy," said Sam and made it more of a routine.

"Saving energy was pretty easy," said Sam and made it more of a routine.

Using Public Transportation: “Public transportation helps reduce emissions,” said Captain Planet. Instead of driving, Sam took buses and trains, reducing their carbon footprint.

"This was a smarter way to travel," said Sam while they enjoyed their journey.

Reducing Plastic Use: "Plastic littering the environment is killing our planet," said Captain Planet. Sam stopped using all single-use plastic and used reusable options instead. "We can all help protect our planet," said Sam proudly holding their reusable water bottle.

Teaching Others: "Please share how to conserve and protect climate change," said Captain Planet. Sam taught their friends how to think about climate change and how everyone can help.

"Together we can make an enormous difference," said Sam feeling empowered to help.

Chapter 14

Life Below Water

Chapter 14: Life Below Water

Marine Biologist Ms. Ocean took Sam below the surface to see the good and bad of life in the ocean.

Beach Cleanups: "Trash is harmful to marine life," Ms. Ocean said as Sam set up beach clean-ups to collect bags full of trash on the beach.

"Cleaning up helps the ocean, said Sam, who felt proud of what they were doing.

Coral Reefs: "Coral reefs are important," Ms. Ocean said, as Sam safeguarded the underwater life and discovered ocean life and, their importance to coral reefs.

"These reefs are really beautiful and important," Sam said in shock to see what lay beneath the ocean.

Sustainable Fishing: "It is important to manage fish populations," Ms. Ocean said as Sam supported responsible fishing and sustainable fishing practices.

"That is the best way to feed people and keep our oceans healthy," Sam said, learning about catch limits.

Reducing Plastic Pollution: "There is so much plastic in the ocean," said Ms. Ocean, while Sam went and collected plastic debris from the ocean to help protect life below the surface.

"Every piece we take away from the environment helps," Sam said proudly of what they are doing.

Marine Protected Areas: "These are safe spaces, said Ms. Ocean. It was then, Sam was set to help develop Marine Protected Areas for ocean life to thrive.

"This means an opportunity for ocean life in the future," Sam said with optimism.

Chapter 15

Life On Land

Chapter 15: Life On Land

Ranger Wild led Sam into verdant woods and wild places overflowing with life.

Forest Protection: "Forests are the lungs of the earth," Ranger Wild said. Sam was helping combat deforestation by planting trees to protect natural areas.

"Forests are so precious," Sam said, standing in the shade of large trees.

Wildlife Protection: "Many species are at risk," Ranger Wild said. Sam was able to support issues relating to protecting endangered species.

"We need to keep our wildlife safe," Sam said in response to his kinship with the animals.

Preventing Poaching: Poaching has detrimental effects on wildlife," Ranger Wild said. Sam participated in anti-poaching patrols to keep wildlife safe.

"For sure," Sam said now understanding the value of their mission.

Habitat Restoration: "Habitat restoration helps protect biodiversity," Ranger Wild said. To help introduce life back into areas that had been damaged, Sam was involved in habitat restoration programs.

"That does make a difference," Sam noticed as plants and animals returned.

Sustainability: "We need to use land wisely," Ranger Wild said. Sam stood and advocated for sustainable farming practices that supported the land.

"That's beneficial for nature and us," Sam said watching the benefits of careful land use.

Chapter 16

Peace, Justice, & Strong Institutions

Chapter 16: Peace, Justice, & Strong Institutions

Judge Justice guided Sam to the Court House and Community Centre.

Fair Laws: "Laws should represent everybody," Judge Justice spoke about laws that protect people's rights.

Fair laws "build a legal just society", Sam said beginning to understand their importance.

Ending Violence: "There is no room for violence in our world," Judge Justice said, and Sam got very involved in violence prevention and peace building campaigns.

"Peace is where it starts," Sam agreed and took on his own identity about being safe and putting an end to violence.

Helping Refugees: "Refugees need our help," said Judge Justice. Sam got involved in assisting refugees to find safety and settle down into their new lives.

"Everyone should feel safe and have a place to call home," Sam said, recognizing that everyone had their own past and journey.

Community Programs: "Communities build peace," Judge Justice taught. Sam was involved in directing community programming that united people together.

"Where there is unity in the community, there is strength", Sam said while watching everyone embrace their community.

Access to justice: "Everyone should have access to justice," Judge Justice explained. Sam was engaged with programs, such as legal aid, that assisted people to access justice and understand their rights.

"Justice should be accessible and available to everyone," Sam said, feeling elated about empowering the world.

Chapter 17

Partnerships For The Goals

Chapter 17: Partnerships for the Goals

Mr. Unity taught Sam, there is power in working together.

International Cooperation: Mr. Unity said, "Countries working together is what allows us to achieve important things." Sam had seen how world leaders came together on important issues, which is global cooperation.

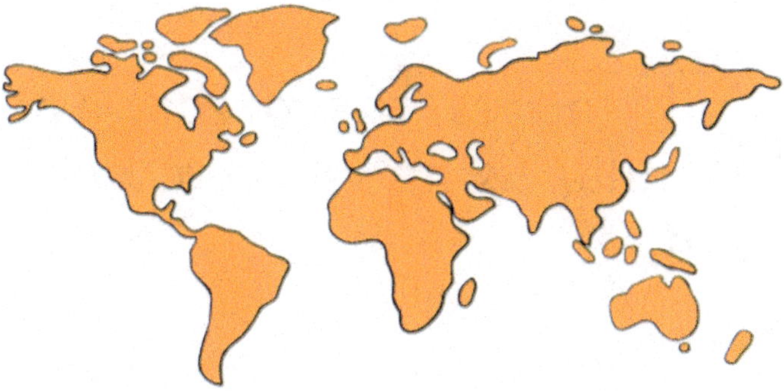

"We can work together to solve Global issues," Sam thought.

Local Collaboration: Mr. Unity told him, "Communities teaming up can do so much more!" Sam became involved with several community groups that worked on Sustainability projects.

"Teamwork makes the dream work," Sam said cheerfully as he worked with everyone as a group.

Shared Resources: Mr. Unity said, "Sharing resources supports everyone." Sam helped share the resources - food, and medical supplies to communities that needed.

"We are helping other people. That is what it is all about," Sam said thoughtfully on shared generosity.

Education for All: Mr. Unity stated, "We need to educate everyone about those goals," Sam taught his friends and neighbors about the Sustainable Development Goals.

"Knowledge is power," Sam said while sharing the education.

Celebrating Our Achievements: Mr. Unity said to Sam, "We have to celebrate our achievements." Sam took part in a local celebration of their achievements towards the Goals.

"This is how a celebration looks!" Sam thought while he felt the happiness of everyone.

As the adventure came towards an end, Sam returned home feeling fulfilled, hopeful, and determined. "I can make a change," Sam reflected! He realized no action is too small and every small action counts!

In his Grandmother's attic, Sam shut the big book with intent to share what he learned.

"We can also help achieve the Global Goals", Sam exclaimed. Sam offered some ideas for family and friends to get involved. Sam's journey through the World of Global Goals ignited a journey to create a better and brighter future for all.

Conservation Journal

Conservation journals allow us to keep track of and document nature, animals, litter, pollution, and plants around us. We have the opportunity to document our observations, learn from what we see, and share those observations with the world. In using our journals, we can see what we are doing to contribute to conservation, propose better ways to improve, and advocate wildlife conservation to our friends and family.

Week________

Sun.____

Mon.____

Tue.____

Wed.____

Thur.____

Fri.____

Sat.____

IDEAS:

Week_______

Sun.____

Mon.____

Tue.____

Wed.____

Thur.____

Fri.____

Sat.____

IDEAS:

Week_______

Sun.____

Mon.____

Tue.____

Wed.____

Thur.____

Fri.____

Sat.____

IDEAS:

Week________

Sun.____

Mon.____

Tue.____

Wed.____

Thur.____

Fri.____

Sat.____

IDEAS:

Week_______

Sun.____

Mon.____

Tue.____

Wed.____

Thur.____

Fri.____

Sat.____

IDEAS:

Week_______

Sun.____

Mon.____

Tue.____

Wed.____

Thur.____

Fri.____

Sat.____

IDEAS:

Week________

Sun.____

Mon.____

Tue.____

Wed.____

Thur.____

Fri.____

Sat.____

IDEAS:

Week_______

Sun.____

Mon.____

Tue.____

Wed.____

Thur.____

Fri.____

Sat.____

IDEAS:

Week_______

Sun.____

Mon.____

Tue.____

Wed.____

Thur.____

Fri.____

Sat.____

IDEAS:

Week________

Sun.____

Mon.____

Tue.____

Wed.____

Thur.____

Fri.____

Sat.____

IDEAS:

Week_______

Sun.____

Mon.____

Tue.____

Wed.____

Thur.____

Fri.____

Sat.____

IDEAS:

About The Author

Daniel Thomas is a talented and accomplished young author with a passion for conservation and community service. As an Eagle Scout and recipient of numerous awards, including America's Top Ten Young Scientist and the EPA 50th Anniversary Award, Daniel has a wealth of experience and knowledge to share with his readers. Daniel is also the recipient of the Youth Volunteer of the Year award for community service, DoD STEM Leadership Award, and Lockheed Martin Leadership Award. In his writing, he draws on his own authentic life experiences and provides readers with easy, practical ways to make a difference in their environment.

In addition to his writing and environmental activism, Daniel is also an honor roll student, avid video game enthusiast, and a talented piano player. He lives in the Dallas Fort Worth area with his family and faithful dog, Minion. Through his writing and community involvement, Daniel aims to inspire and empower young readers to make a positive impact in their own communities.

Printed in Dunstable, United Kingdom

88168370R00067